BATMAN BEYOND

INDUSTRIAL REVOLUTION

BATMAN BEYOND
INDUSTRIAL REVOLUTION

ADAM BEECHEN WRITER
RYAN BENJAMIN PENCILLER
JOHN STANISCI INKER

"LEGENDS OF THE DARK KNIGHT: MAX"
EDUARDO PANSICA PENCILLER
EBER FERREIRA INKER

"LEGENDS OF THE DARK KNIGHT: INQUE"
CHRIS BATISTA PENCILLER
RICH PERROTTA INKER

DAVID BARON COLORIST
SWANDS TRAVIS LANHAM LETTERERS
DUSTIN NGUYEN ORIGINAL SERIES COVERS
DARWYN COOKE COLLECTION COVER

BATMAN CREATED BY **BOB KANE**

Chris Conroy Editor – Original Series
Ian Sattler Director – Editorial, Special Projects and Archival Editions
Robin Wildman Editor
Robbin Brosterman Design Director – Books

Eddie Berganza Executive Editor
Bob Harras VP – Editor-in-Chief

Diane Nelson President
Dan DiDio and **Jim Lee** Co-Publishers
Geoff Johns Chief Creative Officer
John Rood Executive VP – Sales, Marketing and Business Development
Amy Genkins Senior VP – Business and Legal Affairs
Nairi Gardiner Senior VP – Finance
Jeff Boison VP – Publishing Operations
Mark Chiarello VP – Art Direction and Design
John Cunningham VP – Marketing
Terri Cunningham VP – Talent Relations and Services
Alison Gill Senior VP – Manufacturing and Operations
David Hyde VP – Publicity
Hank Kanalz Senior VP – Digital
Jay Kogan VP – Business and Legal Affairs, Publishing
Jack Mahan VP – Business Affairs, Talent
Nick Napolitano VP – Manufacturing Administration
Sue Pohja VP – Book Sales
Courtney Simmons Senior VP – Publicity
Bob Wayne Senior VP – Sales

BATMAN BEYOND: INDUSTRIAL REVOLUTION

DC Comics, 1700 Broadway, New York, NY 10019
A Warner Bros. Entertainment Company.
Printed by RR Donnelley, Salem, VA, USA. 12/23/11. First Printing.
ISBN: 978-1-4012-3374-7

DC COMICS
PROUDLY PRESENTS...
LONG AFTER THE ORIGINAL BATMAN
DISAPPEARED, TEENAGER TERRY MCGINNIS
STUMBLED UPON THE RECLUSIVE BRUCE
WAYNE...AND HIS SECRETS. TEMPERED
BY PERSONAL TRAGEDY, AND GIVEN
BRUCE'S BLESSING AND GUIDANCE,
TERRY NOW FIGHTS CRIME IN THE
GOTHAM CITY OF TOMORROW AS

BATMAN
BEYOND

THE LONGER YOU *MUCK* WITH THESE DREGS, THE *BETTER* THE CHANCES OF THEM GETTING *LUCKY.*

SWOKK

TZZZAATTTTT

DON'T WORRY, THAT'S THE *LAST* OF THEM.

AND STOP SLAGGING ON MY *GOOD TIME,* WILL YOU?

THESE LAST COUPLE WEEKS SINCE THAT *HUSH* THING... GOTHAM'S BEEN *NICE* AND *QUIET,* EXCEPT FOR THE OCCASIONAL CHUMPS LIKE *THESE* BOZOS.

IT'S THE ONES THAT *DON'T* KNOW WHAT THEY'RE DOING YOU HAVE TO WATCH OUT FOR.

BOZOS LIKE THOSE CAN *STILL* DO A LOT OF DAMAGE, McGINNIS.

I'D DEBATE YOU, BRUCE, WITH THESE GUYS AS EXHIBIT A, BUT I'M LATE TO MEET *DANA.*

IT'S BEEN *GREAT* HAVING TIME TO SPEND WITH FAMILY AND FRIENDS AGAIN... IT ALMOST FEELS LIKE A *NORMAL LIFE,* YOU KNOW?

NO.

I *WOULDN'T* KNOW THAT FEELING.

JATTS...? YOU *OKAY,* MAN?

THE *WAND*... MUST'VE REACTED WITH ALL THE *CRAP* IN MY BODY...

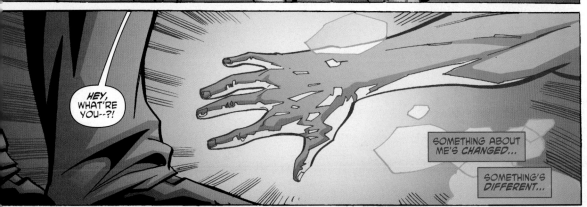

HEY, WHAT'RE YOU--?!

SOMETHING ABOUT ME'S *CHANGED*...

SOMETHING'S *DIFFERENT*...

LEAD.

I TURNED HIM INTO *LEAD.*

THIS... THIS *ISN'T* WHAT I WAS EXPECTING...

GOTTA GET *AWAY*... GOTTA *THINK*...

GOTTA GET *OUT* OF METROPOLIS BEFORE *THEY* COME AFTER ME... BEFORE I'M *READY*...

META HUMAN
EVIDENCE CONFISCATION FACILITY

SECURITY BREACH

ERRNT ERRNT ERRNT ERRNT ERRNT

NOW, WHO WOULD BE *DUMB* ENOUGH TO DO SOMETHING LIKE *THIS?!*

DEPENDING ON WHAT'S BEEN *STOLEN,* FOR THE THIEF'S SAKE...

I'M SO SORRY...!

NO, NO, IT'S *MY* FAULT FOR BEING LATE, AND FOR COMING UP *BEHIND* YOU...

I'M JUST HAPPY TO SEE YOU... EVERYTHING'S BEEN SO... *TREMENDOUS* LATELY.

MOST.

VZEET VZEET VZEET VZEET

I FORGOT HOW MUCH I *HATE* THAT SOUND WHEN WE'RE TOGETHER...

RELAX, D, IT'S JUST MY *MOM*...

MOM? WHAT'S *UP?*

TERRY, DO YOU STILL HAVE YOUR *OLD GOOD SHOES,* OR DID WE GIVE THEM AWAY?

GAVE 'EM AWAY. WHY?

WE'RE AT THE FIELDS-RICH MALL, GETTING YOUR BROTHER HIS *ELEMENTARY SCHOOL GRADUATION SUIT,* AND I GUESS WE'LL ADD SHOES TO OUR LIST.

MATTY'S TRYING ON *SUITS?* LET ME *TALK* TO HIM!

HELLO?

I CAN'T SEE YOU RIGHT NOW, BUT I'M SURE YOU LOOK *RIDICULOUS*.

SHUT UP!

WHAT DID YOU *SAY* TO HIM? HE'S DOING THAT THING WHERE HE'S TRYING *NOT* TO *GIGGLE*, AND THE TAILOR CAN'T MAKE HIS NOTES.

HONEY, YOU'RE NOT GOING TO *WORK* THE NIGHT OF THE CEREMONY, ARE YOU?

I WOULDN'T MISS BEING THERE FOR THE *WORLD*, MOM. LOVE YOU. 'BYE.

SOUNDS LIKE YOU MADE HER A *PROMISE*, TERRY. YOU'VE BEEN PRETTY *GOOD* ABOUT *KEEPING* THEM, LATELY...

I *KNOW* HOW HARD YOU'RE TRYING. AND I WANT YOU TO KNOW IT'S BEEN *NOTICED*. AND *APPRECIATED*.

YOU AND MY FAMILY ARE *WORTH* THE EFFORT, D... I TOOK YOU ALL FOR *GRANTED* FOR A WHILE, BUT I'M *WORKING* ON *KEEPING* MY PRIORITIES STRAIGHT.

NOW, C'MON... I NEED MY *SECRET WEAPON* RIGHT BESIDE ME...

...LET'S GO GET MATTY HIS *GRADUATION PRESENT*.

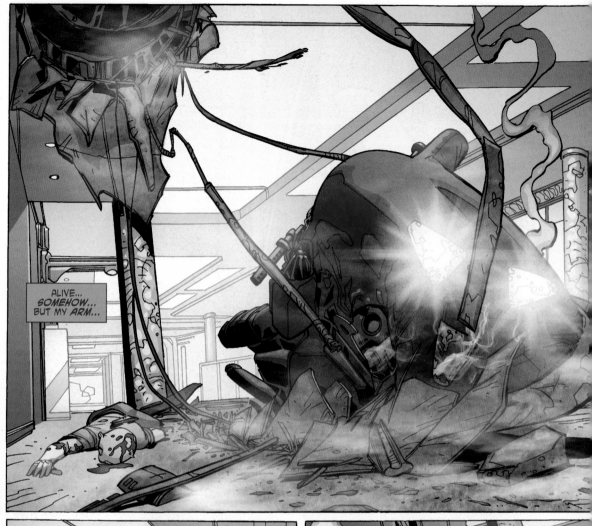

ALIVE... SOMEHOW... BUT MY *ARM*...

AND THE JUSTICE LEAGUE...

...THEY'RE GONNA *FIND* ME...

...SO I GOTTA MAKE IT *HARD* FOR THEM TO GET *TO ME!*

UNLESS YOU WANT ME TO DO TO *YOU* WHAT I DID TO THE *OUTSIDE* OF THIS MALL...

...EVERYBODY STOP!

...WANT TO KNOW HOW OPEN THE SPEEDER'S ENGINE CORE IS TO FUSION AND STABILIZER UPGRADES, BECAUSE WE ARE NOT BUYING THIS ONLY TO HAVE YOU PUT OUT A MODEL IN SIX MONTHS THAT OUTSTRIPS IT FLAT, LIKE THE SIGMA-OH-NINE DID TO THE VENTURE-PLUS PIONEER TWO YEARS AGO...

UH...

LOOKS LIKE A FIRE UPTOWN...

'SCUSE ME FOR A SEC...

...AND WE WANT A GUARANTEE AGAINST OBSOLESCENCE TO THE POINT WHERE, IF THIS COMPANY OR A COMPETITOR COMES OUT WITH A MODEL IN THE NEXT TWO YEARS THAT INCREASES PERFORMANCE BY A FACTOR OF TWO...

BRUCE...?

I ASSUME YOU'RE SEEING SMOKE. POLICE SAY SOMETHING CRASHED INTO A STRUCTURE IN NORTH CENTRAL...

...AND THEN WITNESSES REPORTED THE BUILDING CHANGED ITS COMPOSITION TO SOLID METAL.

WHAT BUILDING?

FIELDS-RICH MALL.

OH, NO...

HE'S *COMPLETELY* SEALED IT OFF. IT'S SHAPING UP AS A MASSIVE *HOSTAGE* SITUATION, BUT NO *DEMANDS* HAVE BEEN MADE YET...

DANA! I'M CRAVING *MONGOLIAN* FOR LUNCH... I'LL GO PICK SOME UP. YOU GOT IT UNDER CONTROL HERE?

TOTAL CONTROL. TAKE YOUR TIME.

I *LOVE* MY *SECRET WEAPON.*

IF THE HOSTAGE-TAKER IS A *TRANSMUTER*, WE COULD BE LOOKING AT A *LOT* OF CIVILIAN COLLATERAL DAMAGE BEFORE THIS IS OVER, IF WE'RE NOT *CAREFUL.*

MY *MOTHER* AND *BROTHER* ARE IN THE MALL!

...

DAMN.

TERRY... CAN YOU BE *OBJECTIVE* ABOUT THIS SITUATION, TREAT IT LIKE *ANY OTHER* AND DO *WHATEVER* NEEDS TO BE DONE?

GOD, BRUCE...

...COULD *YOU?*

MYRICK HERE, COMMISSIONER GORDON...WE'VE SET UP A *PERIMETER* AROUND THE MALL, OUR BASE IS A *ROOFTOP* ACROSS THE STREET.

OUR SCANS INDICATE THE MALL FACADE HAS BEEN TRANSMUTED INTO *POLYTRITANIUM*, WE'RE NOT SURE *HOW* THICK.

WE'RE ALSO NOT SURE HOW THE SUSPECT IS GETTING AIR INTO THE BUILDING FOR THE *HOSTAGES*.

MAYBE *MINUTE PINPRICKS* SOMEWHERE IN THE STRUCTURE WE HAVEN'T LOCATED YET, OR MAYBE THERE'S AN *UNDERGROUND* SOURCE.

WHATEVER THE VENTILATION SOURCE, *FIND* IT, MYRICK. IT MIGHT BE OUR *ONLY* WAY IN.

BUT FOR GOD'S SAKE, BE *DISCREET*...I DON'T WANT *ANYTHING* SETTING THIS NEW FREAK OFF!

IS THERE ANY SIGN OF *BATMAN*?

NEGATIVE. AND GIVEN THAT WE HAVE SEEN NO CAPE PRESENCE THUS FAR, I SUGGEST WE MAKE THIS A STRICTLY *GCPD* OPERATION...

A *TYPICALLY* TERRIBLE HUMAN SUGGESTION.

HAVE YOUR TOY SOLDIERS *STAND DOWN*, OFFICER...

...THE JUSTICE LEAGUE WILL HANDLE THINGS FROM HERE.
GREEN LANTERN
AQUAGIRL
BARDA
MICRON
WARHAWK

STAND *WITH* US OR STAND *DOWN*, BATMAN.

THERE'S A MALL FULL OF *HOSTAGES* BEHIND YOU, AND WE DON'T HAVE TIME FOR *GAMES*.

I KNOW. MY *MOTHER* AND *BROTHER* ARE TWO OF THOSE HOSTAGES.

AND I HEARD ENOUGH ON THE WAY HERE TO KNOW THEIR *CAPTOR* WOULDN'T BE *IN* THERE IF IT WASN'T FOR THE JUSTICE LEAGUE.

THE *LAST* THING I WANT TO DO IS LET *THESE* TWIPS PUT MY FAMILY AT ANY *MORE* RISK.

YOU'RE OUT OF BOUNDS. *MY* CITY, *MY* PROBLEM.

WELL *PUT*, McGINNIS.

BUT WE KNOW THEY'RE *NOT* GOING TO BACK OFF.

OKAY, WE'VE *TRAINED* FOR THIS. YOU *KNOW* HOW TO BEAT THE JUSTICE LEAGUE.

YOU'VE GOT TO STRIKE *FIRST*.

START WITH THE ONE WITH THE WEAPON THAT CAN DESTROY THE *UNIVERSE*.

YOU...

A *SUCKER PUNCH?* THAT'S LOW FOR *ANYONE,* BUT FROM A SO-CALLED *"SUPERHERO...?!"*

THE ONES WITH THE *TEMPERS* WILL BE NEXT...

YOU DON'T *DESERVE* THE MIGHT OF MY *MEGA-ROD,* TRAITOR, BUT THAT'S WHAT YOU WILL *GET!*

FIGURE *BARDA* FIRST.

HRRARR!

LET HER GET IN *CLOSE.* YOU CAN'T REALLY *HURT* HER...

SHZAKK

G-G-G-G-G-G...

...BUT THE *FULL CHARGE* FROM THE *SUIT* WILL GIVE HER SOMETHING TO *THINK* ABOUT.

YOU OKAY?

ASIDE FROM CATCHING THE WORLD'S WORST CASE OF FULL-BODY ATHLETE'S FOOT, I'M ACES.

GOT ACCESS TO THE BELT?

YEP.

HIS REINFORCEMENTS SHOULD BE ON THE WAY, AND THEY WON'T BE BEING CAREFUL.

GIVE HIM A QUICK HIT OF FOUR THOUSAND DEGREES BY THE WAY, THE SUIT'S RADAR SHOWS BARDA AND WARHAWK INCOMING FROM THE EAST.

YEEEOWW!

EAST'S THAT WAY, RIGHT?

IT IS.

BUT YOU'VE STILL GOT THE TOUGHEST ONE TO FACE.

OOF!

KRASSHHOOM

THE ONE YOU *LIKE*.

BATMAN...? THIS ISN'T LIKE YOU, TO FIGHT OVER *JURISDICTION* WHEN *LIVES* ARE ON THE LINE...

UNLESS...ARE SOME OF THE PEOPLE IN THERE PEOPLE YOU *KNOW*?

YOU'VE GOT TO GO *AT* HER, TERRY...

I... I....

GO AT HER!

I HOPE WHEN THIS IS ALL *OVER*, YOU'LL FEEL LIKE YOU CAN *TALK* TO ME.

BUT RIGHT NOW...

FOOOSHH

...THERE'S TOO MUCH AT *STAKE*...

...AND *NO* TIME FOR *CONVERSATION*.

McGINNIS...? *McGINNIS!*

"WHAT'S GOING ON THERE?"

HERE'S HOW THIS IS GOING TO WORK, EVERYONE...

I'VE SEALED UP ALL THE EXITS, TURNED THE OUTSIDE OF THE MALL TO POLYTRITANIUM, AND NO SIGNALS CAN GET OUT.

I DON'T WANT TO HURT ANYBODY, SO IF WE ALL JUST STAY HERE IN THIS ONE AREA, EVERYTHING WILL BE FINE.

YOU DON'T LOOK SO HEALTHY, MAN... AND THERE'S A LOT MORE OF US THAN YOU...

YOU'VE SEEN WHAT I CAN DO...

...IF YOU WANT TO RISK TOUCHING ME, MAKE YOUR MOVE.

NO ONE'S GOING TO TOUCH YOU, BUT YOUR PLAN CAN'T BE TO KEEP US ALL IN HERE FOREVER...

DO YOU HAVE ANY DEMANDS?

MISS...? WAS THERE ANYTHING *ELSE*...?

SURELY YOU WEREN'T THINKING OF ASKING FOR AN EVEN *LOWER* PRICE THAN WE GAVE YOU, BECAUSE WE COULDN'T--

NO, I'M WAITING FOR MY *BOYFRIEND*...HE *SAID* HE WAS GOING TO GET *FOOD*, BUT THAT WAS, LIKE, *FOREVER* AGO...

AH...WELL...IN *THAT* CASE, IF YOU HAVE SOME *EXTRA* TIME, AND SINCE YOU'VE SAVED *SO* MUCH MONEY, MY MANAGER SUGGESTED I DISCUSS SOME OPTIONAL *UPGRADES* FOR YOUR NEW SPEEDER--

--BUT I'LL JUST TELL HIM YOU WEREN'T INTERESTED...

GOODWIN JR SPEEDERS

DON'T PANIC...

NICE WORK, AQUAGIRL...

FORGET HIM. WE HAVE A MALL-TURNED-FORTRESS TO BREACH AND HOSTAGES TO FREE...

RAISING SUIT SURFACE TEMP... BE READY WITH THE BOOT JETS.

SKROOOM

--UH!

WHAT NOW?

THE GREEN BRAT SHOULD BE ABOUT READY TO WAKE UP...

SEE THAT HE DOESN'T.

KLOKK

OHH...

WAIT, THIS IS RIDICULOUS... I COULD BE AT IT WITH THESE GUYS FOR HOURS...

...WHILE WHOEVER'S IN THAT MALL IS DOING WHO KNOWS WHAT TO MOM AND MATT...

MCGINNIS... THE *GOTHAM ELEVATED TRAIN* USED TO RUN UNDER THAT MALL...

SCHWAY!

THE MALL'S OLD *EL* STATION...

YEAH, WE *THOUGHT* OF THAT, BUT IT WAS SEALED UP *DECADES* AGO.

SURE, BUT DID THEY SEAL IT WITH *POLYTRITANIUM?*

COME ON! *PLAN* IN THE WORKS!

SUBWAY

I CAN'T BELIEVE WE'RE *FOLLOWING* THIS GUY...

...OR TURN IT INTO SOMETHING EVEN *BETTER*...

CELL BY CELL... *FOCUS*...

EEEYAAAAAH!!

YES... YES...

IT *WORKED*... AND I CAN *SEE* IT NOW... *ALL* OF WHAT I CAN DO...

...AND ALL OF *YOU*... ALL OF YOU ARE JUST DISTRACTIONS...

AND I DON'T *NEED* DISTRACTIONS...

...BUT I *DO* NEED HOSTAGES...

SO FAR, SO GOOD...

GOOD, *HOW?* I'VE GOT *RAT POOP* ALL OVER MY BOOTS.

GOOD, AS IN THIS GUY JATTS *DIDN'T* TURN THE TUNNELS INTO SOLID *IRON* OR SOMETHING.

YOU DON'T KNOW *HOW* GOOD A SIGN THIS IS, McGINNIS... I'M REVIEWING THE *FILES.*

WE WERE *DAMNED LUCKY* OVER THE YEARS WITH THE VARIOUS *IDIOTS* WHO USED *MENTACHEM* AT ONE TIME OR ANOTHER...

THEY WERE ALL *COMPLETELY* INCOMPETENT, AND ALL OF THEM WERE *STILL* AMONG THE *MOST* POWERFUL FOES WE FACED.

IF *ANY* OF THEM HAD REALIZED THE *TRUE SCOPE* OF THEIR POWERS...

I GET IT.

I HOPE YOU DO. THIS NUT NEEDS TO BE TAKEN DOWN, TERRY.

YOU'VE *GOT* TO MAKE HIM *PRIORITY ONE,* EVEN OVER YOUR *FAMILY.*

IF JATTS FIGURES OUT HIS *POTENTIAL,* YOUR MOTHER AND BROTHER...AND *EVERYONE* ELSE ON THE PLANET, MOST LIKELY...ARE *GONERS.*

MALL EXIT.

HOLD *UP,* TROOPS. LOOKS LIKE THIS IS *IT.*

GOT A LITTLE *AGGRESSION* YOU WANT TO WORK OUT?

I THINK WE MIGHT BE ABLE TO SCROUNGE SOME UP.

KKRAKK ZZAMMM

THANKS FOR-- WHOA--GETTING THEM TO LISTEN TO ME, BACK THERE.

OF COURSE. I JUST WISH YOU HAD TOLD US YOU NEEDED HELP *SOONER*, SO THE FIGHTING COULD HAVE BEEN *AVOIDED*.

YEAH... I DON'T *TRUST* TOO MANY PEOPLE, I GUESS...

WELL, IF YOU *NEED* A PERSON YOU CAN TRUST...

...I HOPE YOU WILL CONSIDER *ME*.

WE'RE THROUGH!

LOOKS LIKE IT GOES ALL THE WAY UP...

EXCELLENT. LET *ME* GO FIRST...

...AND BE READY TO *FAN OUT* AS SOON AS WE HIT THE--

WELCOME...

...I HAVE FACED THE *OMEGA EFFECT* OF *DARKSEID* AND LIVVVVV...

WHEREAS *I'M* A NORMAL HUMAN JUST LIKE *YOU,* MR. JATTS...

...JUST *BIGGER!*

BOONT

AND SO LONG AS I PIN YOUR *HANDS...*

YOU FOOL, THE POWER'S NOT *IN* MY HANDS...

EEEYAHHH!

SSZZZZSS

...IT'S IN *ME!*

HAVE SOME *PHOSPHORUS!*

DO WHAT YOU CAN FOR *MICRON,* AQUAGIRL... LANTERN, FIND A *WEAK SPOT* IN THE POLYTRITANIUM AROUND THE MALL, AND BUST IT *OPEN* SO WE CAN GET SOME *HELP* IN HERE!

FOOSHH

THIS IDIOT IS *WARHAWK'S* PREY NOW!

OKAY, THAT'S *ALL* OF THEM OUT OF THE LINE OF FIRE, FOR *NOW*.

HOW DO WE GET THEM *OUT* OF THIS?

WHAT KIND OF *METAL* DOES IT LOOK LIKE TO YOU?

MAYBE *COPPER*... SHOULD I USE THE SUIT'S *SONICS* TO CRACK IT OFF THEM?

TOO *RISKY*. I THINK IT'LL HAVE TO BE *CHIPPED* OFF... *CAREFULLY*.

I'LL DO IT... HOWEVER LONG IT *TAKES*.

CHNK

THEY'LL BE *FINE* WHERE THEY ARE FOR NOW. GET BACK TO THE *JUSTICE LEAGUE* AND HELP THEM.

BRUCE, I'M *NOT* LEAVING MY *FAMILY*--!

I *UNDERSTAND* HOW YOU FEEL, BUT THEY'RE *SAFER* LIKE THIS, CAN'T WANDER INTO *HARM'S WAY*. NOW YOU CAN FOCUS ON THE *ENEMY*...

FORMER POLICE DETECTIVE *BEN SINGLETON* HELD *FIRM* ON HIS ALLEGATION THAT *RICHARD GRAYSON* POSED AS *NIGHTWING* FOR SEVERAL YEARS...

DAMN.

...CITING A *COMMISSIONER'S OFFICE CONFESSION* BY AN "*INTERESTED PARTY*" IN THE RECENT *HUSH* KILLINGS...

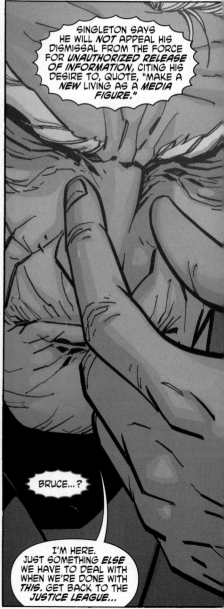

SINGLETON SAYS HE WILL *NOT* APPEAL HIS *DISMISSAL* FROM THE FORCE FOR *UNAUTHORIZED RELEASE OF INFORMATION*, CITING HIS DESIRE TO, QUOTE, "*MAKE A NEW* LIVING AS A *MEDIA FIGURE*."

BRUCE...?

I'M *HERE*. JUST SOMETHING *ELSE* WE HAVE TO DEAL WITH WHEN WE'RE DONE WITH *THIS*. GET BACK TO THE *JUSTICE LEAGUE*...

UUUUGH... AAH!

WHAT'S THE *MATTER* WITH HIM? I DIDN'T HIT HIM *THAT* HARD...

...AND WHY'S HE CLUTCHING HIS *GUT?* I DIDN'T HIT HIM *THERE!*

I DON'T KNOW... MAYBE THE REACTION OF THE *MENTACHEM WAND* HE TOUCHED WITH THE *POISONS* INSIDE HIS BODY IS *CONTINUING...*

OH, GOD... I CAN *FEEL* IT, BURNING ME *OUT* FROM *INSIDE...*

...DON'T HAVE LONG...

CAN I SAY THIS *DOESN'T* LOOK GOOD?

READING BIG *ENERGY SPIKES* HERE...STAY AS FAR OUT OF RANGE AS YOU *CAN...*

BE READY FOR *ANYTHING...*

AAAAAAA!!!

"*WRONG. YOU'VE GOT THE JUSTICE LEAGUE.*"

SsSSHH **SSPLISH** **SSSSSHHHT**

"MAKE *THEM* WORK FOR YOU."

YEAH... *YEAH!*

WARHAWK! YOU AND *MICRON* DISTRACT MATTER MASTER...MAKE HIM *BURN ENERGY!*

WHAT ARE WE...*RODEO CLOWNS?!*

JUST *DO IT!*

LANTERN, *FORGET* THAT!

NNNGH... *EH?*

CAN YOU FOCUS ENOUGH TO CREATE SOME SIMPLE, HEAVY-DUTY CONTAINMENT?

I...I DO NOT KNOW...

WELL, EITHER YOU *WILL* OR WE'LL ALL *DIE.*

SCHWAY.

ANY IDEA HOW MUCH *LONGER* WE'RE GOING TO HAVE TO DO THIS?

I'VE *NEVER* DONE MUCH *RUNNING AWAY* BEFORE... FIGHTING DEFENSIVELY IS *NOT* MY PREFERRED TACTIC.

TZZAMM

TZARKK

NOR *OURS*, ONCE I DISPOSE OF THIS *FOUNTAIN*...

SPLSSH

KOOOMM

I SEE YOUR *PLAN*, BARDA... I'M HYDRATED ENOUGH TO HELP A *LITTLE*...

EEEEEEEEEEEEI!

ALL CONTRIBUTIONS IN THE JUSTICE LEAGUE ARE *EQUAL*, AQUAGIRL... HERE IS *MINE* FOR THIS BATTLE.

TOOOM

CONTAIN YOURSELF, WARHAWK... THE BOY HAS NOT GIVEN US HIS *ANSWER* YET.

WELL, BATMAN...? ARE WE *GOOD* ENOUGH FOR YOU?

DON'T *DO* IT, McGINNIS... YOU CAN BE LOYAL TO *JUSTICE* WITHOUT PLEDGING YOURSELF TO SOME *LEAGUE.*

DON'T *ANSWER* TO ANYONE, DON'T *OWE* ANYONE, AND YOU WON'T HAVE TO *COMPROMISE* FOR ANYONE.

YOU FORGET HOW MANY TIMES THE LEAGUE HELPED *YOU.*

PARDON?

NOTHING. I'M *IN...* PROVISIONALLY. I'VE GOT SOME *CONDITIONS.*

ONE, IF YOU *NEED* ME FOR SOMETHING, IT BETTER BE *BIG,* BECAUSE FOR *ME,* THIS CITY IS *JOB ONE.*

TWO, IF YOU'RE GOING ON A MISSION AND I *SAY* I'M BUSY, I'M *BUSY.*

THREE, GOTHAM'S *OFF-LIMITS* UNLESS I *ASK* FOR YOUR HELP.

...

...ACTUALLY, THOSE ARE PRETTY GOOD CONDITIONS.

WE *ACCEPT* YOUR TERMS, BATMAN. *WELCOME* TO THE *JUSTICE LEAGUE.*

SHAKE HIS *HAND,* WARHAWK.

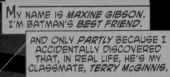
MY NAME IS *MAXINE GIBSON.* I'M BATMAN'S *BEST FRIEND.*

AND ONLY *PARTLY* BECAUSE I ACCIDENTALLY DISCOVERED THAT, IN REAL LIFE, HE'S MY CLASSMATE, *TERRY McGINNIS.*

FACT IS, TERRY AND I WOULD BE BEST FRIENDS EVEN IF HE *WASN'T* BATMAN.

BUT HE IS, SO THAT MAKES OUR FRIENDSHIP A LITTLE *DIFFERENT.*

BEING BATMAN'S BEST FRIEND MEANS I *HELP HIM OUT.*

NO, I DON'T PUT ON A *CAPE* AND *SHORT SHORTS,* FIGHT CRIME WITH HIM, AND SAY THINGS LIKE, "HOLY BAD PUNS, BATMAN!"

PLEASE.

I'M KIND OF HIS *EYES* AND *EARS,* DOING WHAT I CAN WITH *COMPUTERS* TO HELP HIM GET THINGS DONE.

BUT EVEN THEN, IT'S *MORE* THAN THAT.

BEING BATMAN'S BEST FRIEND MEANS *KEEPING SECRETS...*

...OCCASIONALLY HAVING TO DO THINGS *WAY OUT OF YOUR COMFORT ZONE...*

MAXINE GIBSON, FRIEND OF BATMAN, PREPARE TO BEAR WITNESS...

HAMILTON HILL HIGH SCHOOL

BEING BATMAN'S BEST FRIEND ALSO MEANS *COVERING* FOR HIM.

WHICH HAPPENS A *LOT*.

--*STOMACH VIRUS*, MR. NOVICK. TERRY ASKED ME TO PICK UP HIS HOMEWORK *FOR* HIM.

DANA!

SOMETIMES IT'S *HARDER* THAN OTHERS. LIKE WITH HIS *GIRLFRIEND*.

TERRY TOLD ME TO TELL YOU--

HI, MAX... LISTEN, I'M *NOT* INTERESTED IN *ANYTHING* TERRY HAS TO SAY. NOT RIGHT NOW.

I'VE GOT *BIGGER* PROBLEMS TO DEAL WITH. AND TERRY'S *NOT* AROUND TO HELP.

AGAIN.

BEING BATMAN'S BEST FRIEND MEANS SOMETIMES *I* HAVE A DOUBLE LIFE, TOO.

PAXTON POWERS, PRISONER TANGO-BRAVO-HOTEL ONE-NINER-FOUR-FOUR.

COLLECT YOUR THINGS AND REPORT FOR YOUR GATE MONEY. YOU'RE *RELEASED.*

HUH?

RELEASED? MY NEXT *PAROLE HEARING* ISN'T FOR *SEVEN MONTHS.* HOW--?

ABOVE MY *PAY GRADE,* FREEBIE. CALL YOUR *LAWYER.*

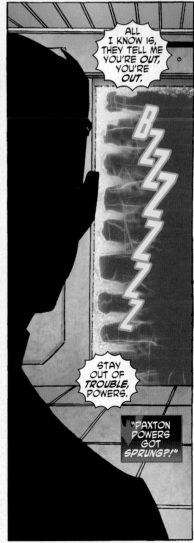

ALL I KNOW IS, THEY TELL ME YOU'RE *OUT,* YOU'RE *OUT.*

BZZZZZ

STAY OUT OF *TROUBLE,* POWERS.

"PAXTON POWERS GOT *SPRUNG?!*"

WAYNE MANOR.

WAYNE INDUSTRIES, WAYNETECH, WAYNE-POWERS, WE'VE *NEVER* HAD LABOR PROBLEMS OF *ANY* KIND. IF ANYTHING, WE'VE--

YEAH, NOT THE BEST TIME FOR A *HISTORY* LESSON RIGHT NOW, BRUCE...

FINE. *YOU* KNOW *CROWD CONTROL* PROTOCOLS.

GO TO WORK.

TEAR GAS *AWAY.*

SEEMS A *SHAME* TO DUMP IT ON *YOUR* SECURITY GUYS... THEY'RE ACTUALLY SHOWING SOME *RESTRAINT.*

FOOOSSHH

CAN'T COUNT ON *THAT* LASTING. ONLY A MATTER OF *TIME* BEFORE SOMETHING *BREAKS.*

SPEAKING OF WHICH... ...LOOKS LIKE SOMETHING'S BREAKING *OUTSIDE* THE GAS PERIMETER.

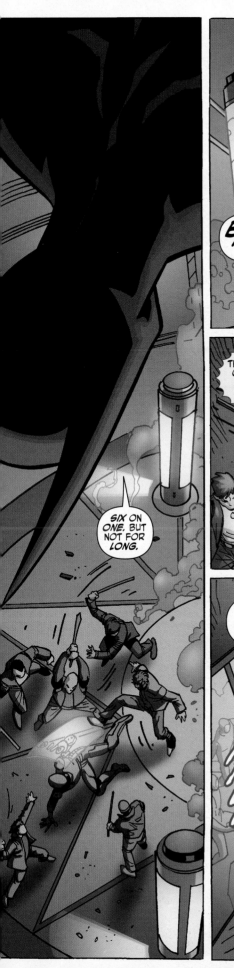

HEY! EVERYONE SLOW-PULSE IT!

BATMAAAAN!

CAREFUL...

REMEMBER, THESE *AREN'T* META-CRIMINALS, THEY'RE *NORMAL PEOPLE.* YOU'RE THEIR *PROTECTOR.*

SIX ON ONE, BUT NOT FOR LONG.

HE'S JUST A STOOGE FOR *WAYNE! GET HIM!*

KREESHH

THEN I GUESS THIS IS WHAT YOU MIGHT CALL *IRONIC.*

YOU MAKE A *REALLY* GOOD TEAR GAS.

ALFRED CAME UP WITH IT. ALWAYS *WAS* A GREAT COOK.

GO *DARK* FOR NOW AND GET *OUT* OF THERE...

THE *POLICE* CAN HANDLE THE CLEANUP, AND WE DON'T NEED TO SIT AROUND WHILE THEY WRITE *REPORTS*...

OKAY, WHAT DO YOU WANT ME TO DO *NOW?*

NOTHING.

I KNOW WHAT *THAT* MEANS.

WHAT ARE *YOU* GOING TO DO NOW?

...FINANCIAL STORY OF THE DAY CONTINUES TO BE THE STEEP DECLINE IN WAYNE-POWERS STOCK...

TAKE A *PERSONAL* ROLE IN THE UNION NEGOTIATIONS.

PAXTON POWERS GETTING OUT, THEN OUT OF *NOWHERE* CONTRACT TALKS HIT THE SKIDS...? *CAN'T* BE A COINCIDENCE.

POWERS' DAD DEREK *STOLE* BRUCE'S BUSINESS, THEN ACCIDENTALLY TURNED *HIMSELF* INTO AN IRRADIATED MENACE NAMED *BLIGHT* BEFORE GOING DOWN WITH THE SHIP...*LITERALLY.*

PAXTON TOOK *OVER* FOR HIS OLD MAN, BUT THE APPLE DIDN'T FALL FAR FROM THE TREE AND WE SENT *HIM* AWAY.

I'M SURE HE'S BEEN NURSING A *GRUDGE* ALL THIS TIME AND WOULD *LOVE* TO--

TERRY?

HEY, DANA--

SORRY I KEPT YOU *WAITING*...

WHAT'S *UP?* YOU SAID AT SCHOOL IT WAS *URGENT*...

YEAH...I KNOW...I'VE BEEN *AROUN* THE *CORNE* FOR HALF A HOUR WORKIN UP MY *NERVE*...

HUH? FOR *WHAT?*

TERRY...

THE AAMES HOTEL.

MR. WAYNE. IT'S A *PLEASURE* TO MEET YOU. HAVE YOU BEEN TO THIS HOTEL BEFORE? I'M TOLD IT'S BEEN *REMODELED.*

I'VE BEEN HERE.

WELL, THEY DID A *LOVELY* JOB. SEE HOW THEY--

MR. *GODFREY.*

WHEN THE EMPLOYEES' UNION'S MANAGEMENT RELATIONS COMMITTEE *FIRED* THEIR CHIEF NEGOTIATOR IN THE MIDDLE OF CONTRACT TALKS WITH MY COMPANY AND NAMED *YOU* HIS REPLACEMENT...

...I DID A LITTLE *RESEARCH.*

YOU AIDED *BIALYAN NATIONALS* IN OVERTHROWING THE REGIME THERE SO THEY COULD NATIONALIZE THEIR *URANIUM* MINES.

BUT *SUSPICIONS* WERE YOU WERE ON THE PAYROLL OF *KORD INDUSTRIES* AT THE TIME, AND THEY WERE ONLY *TOO* HAPPY TO SWOOP IN WHEN BIALYA'S ECONOMY *COLLAPSED* NOT LONG AFTER.

YOU WORKED ON A *CONTINGENCY* BASIS WITH THE EMPLOYEES OF *FASTFILE COMPUTING* IN BUILDING THEIR *STRIKE FUND.*

WHEN THOSE INVESTMENTS *COLLAPSED,* YOU SHOULD HAVE WALKED AWAY WITH *NOTHING,* BUT YOU SOMEHOW BOUGHT A *HOUSE* SIX MONTHS LATER.

OH, COME **ON**, I DON'T CONTROL THE **STOCKS**, MR. WAYNE... AND I'VE NEVER EVEN **MET** ANYONE WHO WORKS FOR KORD.

THE **FACTS** ARE, I HELPED THE BIALYANS GET WHAT THEY WANTED AND **THEY** SCREWED IT UP. I RAISED MORE MONEY FOR THE FASTFILE STRIKERS THAN THEY EVER **DREAMED**, AND THE MARKET **TANKED**.

I'M JUST **VERY** GOOD AT MY JOB. AND I THINK I'VE GOT YOU **SCARED**. YOU'VE SEEN OUR **REVISED** DEMANDS?

ARE YOU HERE WITH AN **OFFER** FOR ME?

YES.

YOUR DEMANDS ARE **RIDICULOUS**. YOU **KNOW** THEY ARE.

THIS ISN'T **ABOUT** DEMANDS. YOU'RE WORKING FOR **SOMEONE ELSE**, SOMEONE WHO WANTS TO **DESTABILIZE** MY COMPANY.

MY OFFER IS **THIS**...

TELL ME **WHO** YOU'RE WORKING FOR, AND I **WON'T** TAKE YOU APART PIECE BY PIECE.

AND THE MANAGEMENT RELATIONS COMMITTEE TOLD ME YOU **DIDN'T** HAVE A SENSE OF HUMOR.

HOPE YOU'LL COME BY NEGOTIATIONS SOMETIME. WE'LL SAVE YOU A **BAGEL**.

IS IT *PAXTON POWERS?*

... NEVER MET *HIM*, EITHER. ISN'T HE IN *PRISON?*

I'LL SHOW MYSELF *OUT.*

OH, ONE *MORE* THING. I *KNEW* A MAN NAMED GODFREY ONCE. A G. GORDON GODFREY.

YES, THE MAN WHO TRIED TO TURN THE POPULATION AGAINST METAHUMANS SEVERAL *DECADES* AGO. I GET THAT QUESTION A *LOT.*

NO, *NO* RELATION. BUT I CERTAINLY ADMIRE HIS *SKILL.*

HAVE A GOOD NIGHT, MR. *WAYNE.*

KLAK

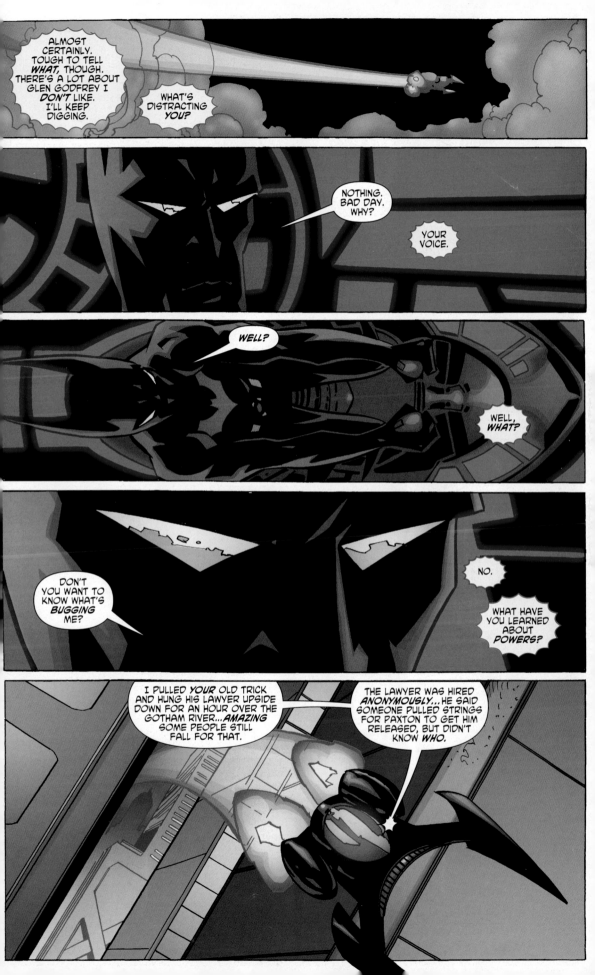

PAXTON'S PAL *ALSO* SET HIM UP WITH SOME *CASH* AND A *SWANK LOFT* ON THE NORTH SIDE.

THE LAWYER SAID PAXTON LOOKED AS BAMBOOZLED AS *ANYONE*, BUT WE *KNOW* PAXTON'S A SNAKE...

THE NORTH SIDE... THAT'S *GENTRIFIED INDUSTRIAL*...WAYNE-POWERS STILL HAS AN *R&D VEHICLE STORAGE FACILITY* THERE...

I KNOW, *I* THOUGHT OF THAT, TOO...I'M HEADED OVER THERE, IF NOTHING ELSE TO LET PAXTON KNOW WE'VE GOT *EYES* ON HIM.

KEEP THE LINE *OPEN*.

GOT A *FEELING?*

GOT A FEELING.

GOT HIM. LOOKS LIKE HE'S GOING INTO YOUR BUILDING. *WHOEVER'S* BEEN HELPING MUST HAVE GIVEN HIM A *KEY*, TOO.

PRETTY *STUPID*... THERE'RE CAMERAS ALL *OVER* THE PLACE.

PARK AND GET IN THERE *AFTER* HIM.

I'M IN. *NICE* NOT TO HAVE TO DEAL WITH *ALARMS* FOR ONCE. PERKS OF WORKING FOR THE *OWNER*.

THERE.

POWERS.

OUT OF PRISON FOR JUST A FEW DAYS, AND *ALREADY* CAUSING TROUBLE?

WH--?

I NEVER FIGURED YOU FOR *SMART*, BUT I THOUGHT YOU WERE SMARTER THAN *THIS*...

BATMAN! NO, IT'S...IT'S NOT WHAT IT *LOOKS* LIKE, I SWEAR...

A WAYNE-POWERS BUILDING IS THE *LAST* PLACE I WANT TO BE...

WHAT'S HE SAYING...?

...BUT WHOEVER GOT ME OUT OF JAIL LEFT *INSTRUCTIONS*... SAID THEY'D MEET ME *HERE* TONIGHT AT THIS EXACT *TIME*...

I THOUGHT I *OWED* IT TO WHOEVER--

IT'S A SET-UP...

GET OUT OF THERE!

TERRY, GET OUT OF THERE NOW!

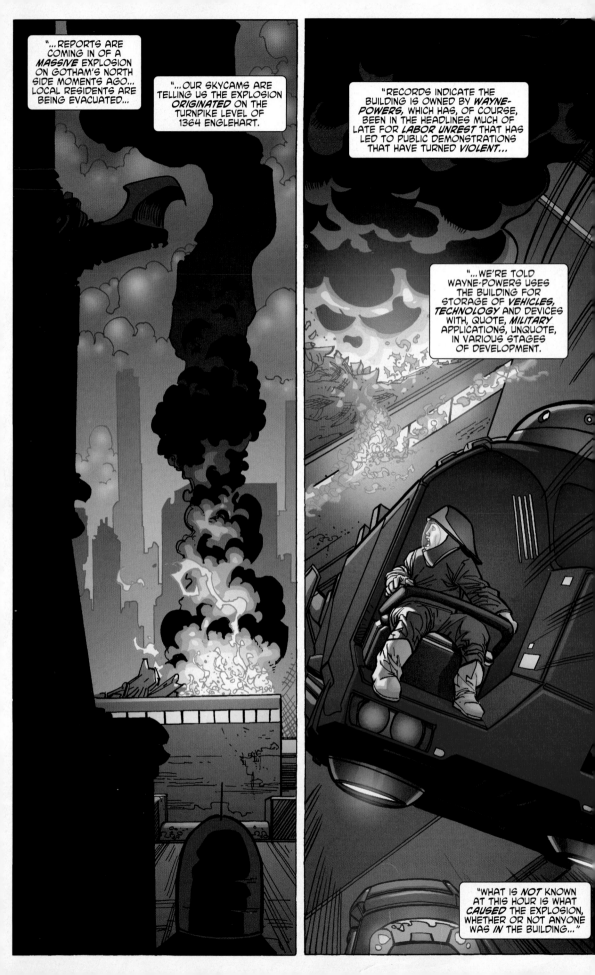

"...REPORTS ARE COMING IN OF A *MASSIVE* EXPLOSION ON GOTHAM'S NORTH SIDE MOMENTS AGO... LOCAL RESIDENTS ARE BEING EVACUATED..."

"...OUR SKYCAMS ARE TELLING US THE EXPLOSION *ORIGINATED* ON THE TURNPIKE LEVEL OF 1364 ENGLEHART."

"RECORDS INDICATE THE BUILDING IS OWNED BY *WAYNE-POWERS*, WHICH HAS, OF COURSE, BEEN IN THE HEADLINES MUCH OF LATE FOR *LABOR UNREST* THAT HAS LED TO PUBLIC DEMONSTRATIONS THAT HAVE TURNED *VIOLENT*..."

"...WE'RE TOLD WAYNE-POWERS USES THE BUILDING FOR STORAGE OF *VEHICLES*, *TECHNOLOGY* AND DEVICES WITH, QUOTE, *MILITARY* APPLICATIONS, UNQUOTE, IN VARIOUS STAGES OF DEVELOPMENT.

"WHAT IS *NOT* KNOWN AT THIS HOUR IS WHAT *CAUSED* THE EXPLOSION, WHETHER OR NOT ANYONE WAS *IN* THE BUILDING..."

UNFORTUNATELY, THIS CRATE WE'RE IN *ISN'T* FUELED UP...

KREESHH

...SO WE BETTER HOPE SOMETHING *ELSE* IN HERE IS!

AND IF THERE *ISN'T?*

POWERS, YOU'RE AN *IDIOT,* BUT YOU'RE NOT *STUPID...*

...DO YOU *REALLY* NEED ME TO ANSWER THAT?

FWOOOOSH

I WANT CHEM ON THE *EAST* AND *NORTH* SIDES!

FOCUS ON LEVEL *SEVEN!* PLANS SAY THAT'S WHERE THE MOST *FLAMMABLE* AND *EXPLOSIVE* STUFF IS!

LET'S GO! WE DON'T WANT ANY *SURPRISES* OR ANYTHING--

"...SOMETIMES, YOU HAVE TO TAKE THE GOOD WITH THE *BAD.*"

BEAUTIFUL, ISN'T IT, DOCTOR FRENCH?

I'M MORE CONCERNED WITH YOUR *CONTAINMENT SUIT.*

IT'S HAVING TROUBLE KEEPING PACE WITH THE *PROGRESSION* OF YOUR ILLNESS.

WE NEED TO MAKE SOME *ADJUSTMENTS.*

DO *WHATEVER* YOU HAVE TO DO TO KEEP ME UP AND *MOVING,* OLD FRIEND.

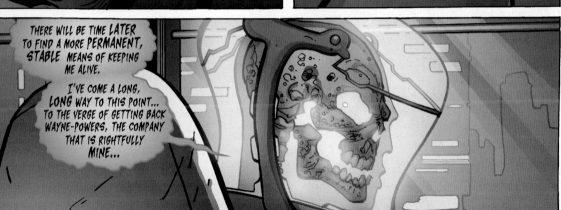

THERE WILL BE TIME *LATER* TO FIND A MORE PERMANENT, *STABLE* MEANS OF KEEPING ME ALIVE.

I'VE COME A LONG, LONG WAY TO THIS POINT... TO THE VERGE OF GETTING BACK WAYNE-POWERS, THE COMPANY THAT IS RIGHTFULLY *MINE*...

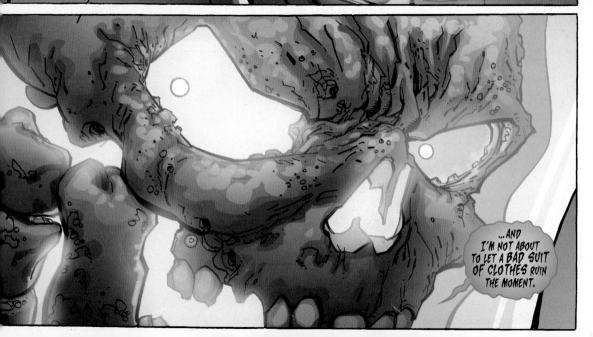

...AND I'M *NOT* ABOUT TO LET A *BAD SUIT* OF CLOTHES RUIN THE MOMENT.

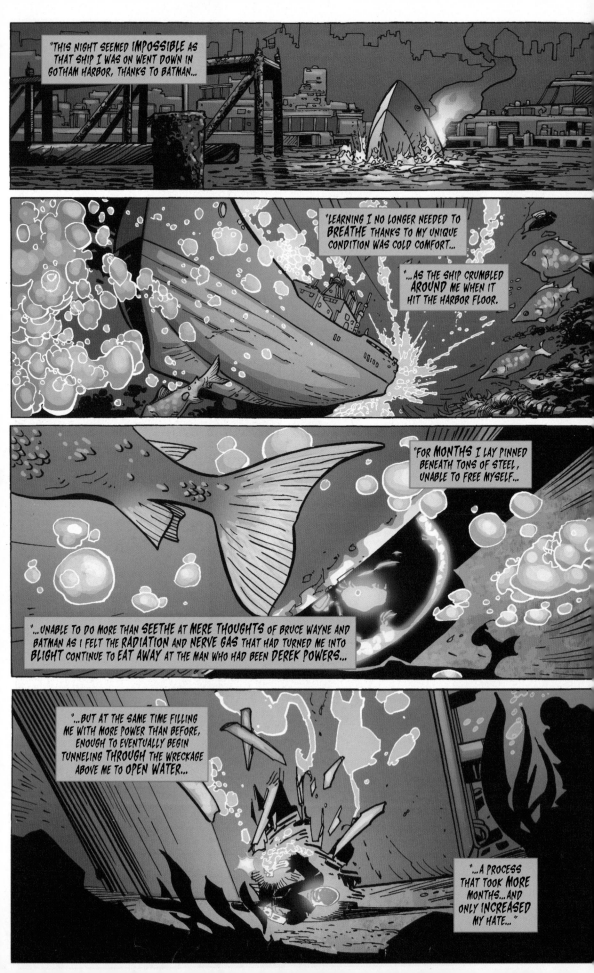

"THIS NIGHT SEEMED IMPOSSIBLE AS THAT SHIP I WAS ON WENT DOWN IN GOTHAM HARBOR, THANKS TO BATMAN..."

"LEARNING I NO LONGER NEEDED TO BREATHE THANKS TO MY UNIQUE CONDITION WAS COLD COMFORT..."

"...AS THE SHIP CRUMBLED AROUND ME WHEN IT HIT THE HARBOR FLOOR."

"FOR MONTHS I LAY PINNED BENEATH TONS OF STEEL, UNABLE TO FREE MYSELF..."

"...UNABLE TO DO MORE THAN SEETHE AT MERE THOUGHTS OF BRUCE WAYNE AND BATMAN AS I FELT THE RADIATION AND NERVE GAS THAT HAD TURNED ME INTO BLIGHT CONTINUE TO EAT AWAY AT THE MAN WHO HAD BEEN DEREK POWERS..."

"...BUT AT THE SAME TIME FILLING ME WITH MORE POWER THAN BEFORE, ENOUGH TO EVENTUALLY BEGIN TUNNELING THROUGH THE WRECKAGE ABOVE ME TO OPEN WATER..."

"...A PROCESS THAT TOOK MORE MONTHS... AND ONLY INCREASED MY HATE..."

"I EMERGED WITH MY PLANS TO RECLAIM ALL I HAD LOST, BURN BRUCE WAYNE TO THE GROUND, AND SHRED THE BATMAN... AND THE OPPORTUNITY TO MAKE THOSE PLANS REALITY.

"AND SO I CAME TO YOU. YOUR SCIENTIFIC GENIUS AND MY BUSINESS ACUMEN HELPED ME RAISE THE MONEY TO BUY WAYNE-POWERS IN THE FIRST PLACE.

"BUT WITH MY... REMOVAL FROM THE COMPANY, YOU TOO HAD BEEN CAST ASIDE."

BUT YOU HELPED KEEP ME ALIVE BY BUILDING THIS SUIT, HELPED ME CONTROL MY GROWING STRENGTH, WHILE I CAUGHT UP ON ALL I HAD-- AAAARGH!

S-SORRY...

IT BURNS AS BADLY AS IT DID DURING THOSE MONTHS YOU BUILT THE SUIT AROUND ME, EACH WELD SEALING MORE OF ME AWAY FROM THE WORLD FOREVER...

...LOCKING ME AWAY WITH MY HATE...

SKREEEEECHH

I DIDN'T EVEN KNOW I STILL *HAD* THIS...

GOOD THING YOU *DID*...

...OTHERWISE I'D BE *EXTRA-CRISPY* RIGHT ABOUT NOW.

THIS STARTING TO MAKE *SENSE* YET?

THE SUDDEN *WORKERS' STRIKE* AT YOUR COMPANY, AN ATTEMPT TO *BLOW UP* THE FORMER OWNER'S SON IN ONE OF YOUR BUILDINGS?

JUST THAT WHOEVER'S TRYING TO *DESTABILIZE* WAYNE-POWERS IS DOING A *HELL* OF A JOB.

STOCKHOLDERS ARE RUNNING FOR THE *HILLS*, AND WHILE I OWN A *CONTROLLING* INTEREST, I DON'T HAVE A *MAJORITY* OF SHARES...

YOU'RE THINKING *WHOEVER* WE'RE UP AGAINST IS GOING TO *GRAB UP* THOSE SHARES, TAKE A MAJORITY AND *STEAL* WAYNE-POWERS.

MOST LIKELY USING *SHELL COMPANIES* TO BUY THE STOCK.

WELL, *MAX* COULDN'T TRACK THE *MONEY* THAT SPRUNG PAXTON BACK TO ITS *SOURCE,* AND I CAN'T USE A *BATARANG* ON THE STOCK MARKET... WHAT'S THE *PLAN?*

I'M GOING TO CALL A *PRESS CONFERENCE* LATER THIS MORNING AND ANNOUNCE THAT AT THE *OPENING BELL* TOMORROW, I'M *BUYING OUT* ALL THE SHAREHOLDERS...

...AND TAKING WAYNE-POWERS *OFF* THE MARKET.

ARE YOU *INSANE?!* IF YOU ANNOUNCE *THAT,* THE STOCKHOLDERS WILL CHARGE YOU THROUGH THE *ROOF!* CAN YOU *AFFORD* THAT?!

AND HAVE YOU THOUGHT WHAT IT'LL DO TO THE MARKET *OVERALL?!* ARE YOU *SURE* YOU WANT TO SAY *THIS?!*

WHAT I *SAY* AND WHAT I *DO* ARE TWO *DIFFERENT* THINGS, MCGINNIS.

AND WHAT I'M DOING IS *LAYING BAIT,* HOPING OUR OPPONENT WILL *PANIC...* LIKE *YOU* JUST DID.

SCHWAY.

VERY, VERY *SCHWAY,* MR. WAYNE.

--DANA AVOIDS ME LIKE THE *PLAGUE* AT SCHOOL, AND SHE WON'T RETURN MY *CALLS*...

IT'S GOING TO TAKE HER SOME *TIME*, TERRY. AND YOUR *BREAKUP* ISN'T THE *ONLY* THING SHE'S DEALING WITH RIGHT NOW.

SHE TOLD ME NOT TO SAY ANYTHING TO ANYONE, *ESPECIALLY* YOU... SHE WANTED TO KEEP THIS *TOTALLY* PRIVATE, BUT...

...SHE TOLD ME HER *BROTHER* IS BACK.

DANA HAS A *BROTHER*?

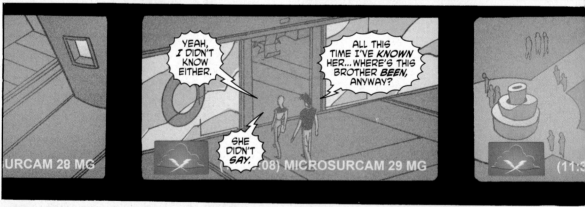

YEAH, *I* DIDN'T KNOW EITHER.

ALL THIS TIME I'VE *KNOWN* HER... WHERE'S THIS BROTHER *BEEN*, ANYWAY?

SHE DIDN'T *SAY*.

URCAM 28 MG

:08) MICROSURCAM 29 MG

(11:3

MY *POINT* IS, GIVE HER SOME *ROOM*.

BUT I *MISS* HER, MAX.

ARE YOU EXPECTING *HAIL* OR SOMETHING? YOU KEEP LOOKING AT THE *CEILINGS*...

OH... THOUGHT I HAD TO *SNEEZE*...THEY SAY LOOKING AT *LIGHT* SOMETIMES HELPS...

THIS IS GOING TO COME DOWN TO A *CHOICE*, YOU KNOW.

KEEP YOUR SECRET AS BATMAN AND *LOSE* HER, OR TELL DANA *EVERYTHING*.

BINGG

OTHERWISE, THIS WILL JUST *KEEP* HAPPENING AGAIN AND AGAIN, AND YOU'LL *NEVER* BE ABLE TO--

--UH...

WHOA! EASY ON THE *TECHWARE!* PROBLEM?

NONE OF YOUR *BUSINESS*.

JUST NEEDS TO *REBOOT*. SO, ANYWAY, THE *CHOICE*.

SLAM

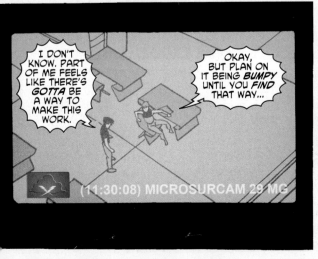

I DON'T KNOW. PART OF ME FEELS LIKE THERE'S *GOTTA* BE A WAY TO MAKE THIS WORK.

OKAY, BUT PLAN ON IT BEING *BUMPY* UNTIL YOU *FIND* THAT WAY...

(11:30:08) MICROSURCAM 29 MG

DANA HAS A *BROTHER?*

"I GUESS I'M NOT THE *ONLY* ONE WHO HAS SECRETS."

SO... DOUG...ARE YOU ENJOYING BEING *BACK,* SO FAR...?

DO YOU MEAN, IS IT BETTER THAN *PRISON?* HA HA, *YES,* OF *COURSE...* IT'S *GREAT* TO BE BACK WITH YOU AND MOM...

AND YOU'VE BEEN SO *WELCOMING.*

YOU KNOW WHAT? I'M GOING TO MAKE US ALL *DINNER...* AS A WAY OF SAYING *"THANK YOU."*

O-OH...

YOU WON'T *BELIEVE* IT, BUT I TURNED OUT TO BE *QUITE* A COOK WHILE I WAS... AWAY.

I'LL GO TO THE STORE. BACK BEFORE YOU *KNOW* IT.

KLIK

HOLA, TURISTA... LOOKING TO DO SOME *SIGHTSEEING*...?

WE GIVE TOURS... *CRAZY* GOOD TOURS...

GOTHAM STOCK EXCHANGE

HARDLY ANYONE AROUND... JUST *MAINTENANCE STAFF* AND A FEW *TRADERS* EARLY FOR WORK...

WISH WE COULD HAVE *AVOIDED* THAT...

...BUT THERE'S NO WAY TO *CLOSE* THE STOCK EXCHANGE--OR *DELAY* THE OPENING BELL--WITHOUT ITS GETTING OUT TO THE *PUBLIC.*

MAYBE WE'LL *LUCK OUT* AND WHOEVER'S BEHIND THIS WON'T *SHOW.*

HE'LL SHOW. HAVE YOU GONE *INVISIBLE* YET?

NAH.

TOO *EARLY.* DON'T WANT TO WASTE THE *POWER.*

TAKE HIM OUT *QUICK* AND YOU WON'T HAVE TO *WORRY* ABOUT IT.

EARLY ENGAGEMENT SHOULD SEND BYSTANDERS *SCATTERING,* TOO. NOW, GO *DARK.*

OKAY, OKAY. MAKING THE *ROUNDS* AGAIN.

THE **NAME** MEANS EVERYTHING. AND WHAT IT **STANDS** FOR.

MY FAMILY MADE THEIR MONEY TO DO **GOOD** THINGS IN THIS WORLD. WHEN I **LOST** THE COMPANY, I **FAILED** THEM. I **LOST** A LITTLE OF THEM.

AND THOUGH I HAD THEIR **HOUSE** AND THE **FUTURE** THEY PROVIDED FOR ME...

...I HAD SO **LITTLE** OF THEM TO BEGIN WITH.

THIS COMPANY MEANS A **LOT** TO YOU, DOESN'T IT? IT MUST'VE HURT BAD WHEN POWERS **TOOK** IT FROM YOU.

THE **COMPANY** MEANS **NOTHING** TO ME.

... DID WE JUST **BOND?**

GO DARK.

NOTHING HAPPENING UP **HERE,** GOOD OR BAD.

UNLESS...

...THIS KIND OF ENERGY EXPENDITURE IS WORTH IT.

SHANNG

TANNG

WHAT ARE YOU--?!

TUNK

FSSSS

FSSSSSSS

MR. POWERS, DON'T!

IS THAT ALL YOU CAN DO? PRETTY SORRY DISPLAY FOR A--

SSSS

BRUCE WAYNE TOOK MY COMPANY FROM ME...YOU TOOK MY FREEDOM AND MY HUMANITY, BATMAN...

MAYBE I CAN'T GET THE LAST TWO BACK, BUT I CAN MAKE SURE YOU DON'T KEEP ME FROM GETTING BACK MY BUSINESS--OR ANYTHING ELSE I WANT-- EVER AGAIN!

MR. POWERS... DEREK... STOP!

FRENCH! DAMMIT--!

NO!

YOUR SUIT HAS BEEN COMPROMISED! IT MAINTAINS YOUR INTEGRITY! THE NERVE GAS AND RADIATION IN YOUR SYSTEM IS CONTINUING TO EAT AWAY AT WHAT'S LEFT OF YOU!

IF WE DON'T RETREAT AND PATCH THAT SUIT, YOU'LL LITERALLY DISSOLVE AND OOZE AWAY!

YOU RESCUED ME FROM A MEANINGLESS WORKADAY LIFE AND GAVE ME PURPOSE AGAIN...

YOU SAVED ME, MR. POWERS... PLEASE, I'M ONLY TRYING TO RETURN THE FAVOR!

VERY WELL, BUT AFTER I DELIVER THE FINAL--

I HOPE YOU'RE PROUD OF YOURSELF, FRENCH... BATMAN'S ESCAPED.

NO MATTER. I CAN KILL HIM ANY TIME I WANT.

JUST LIKE BEFORE THIS HAPPENED TO ME, I CAN DO ANYTHING I WANT.

DOUG...YOU SAID YOU WERE GOING OUT TO GET FOOD TO MAKE *DINNER*...

WHY'D YOU GO ALL THE WAY DOWN... *THERE*?

TOOK A *WRONG TURN*, DANA. DON'T WORRY.

A *WRONG TURN*?! YOU EXPECT ME TO *BELIEVE* THAT?! YOU'RE HOME FOR LESS THAN A *WEEK*, AND PRACTICALLY THE *FIRST* PLACE YOU GO IS BACK TO... TO...

YOU... YOU *HAVEN'T* BEEN TAKING YOUR MEDICATION, HAVE YOU? WERE YOU *FAKING* IT THE WHOLE TIME YOU WERE IN PRISON?!

I SAID, "*DON'T WORRY*."

YES, I *LIED* TO YOU, BUT ONLY BECAUSE I KNEW YOU WOULDN'T *UNDERSTAND*. ALL I DID WAS *VISIT*. I WANTED TO *TEST* MYSELF, SEE IF I *STILL* WANTED TO BE JUST ANOTHER ONE OF THE JOKERZ.

BUT I *DON'T*. I *PASSED* THE TEST. I'M *JUST* WHO I WANT TO BE. SO *RELAX*, LITTLE SISTER.

WHEN THERE'S SOMETHING TO WORRY ABOUT...

...*BELIEVE* ME, I'LL LET YOU KNOW.

BRUCE?

BRUCE? ACE?

HELLO?

MCGINNIS.

BRUCE, I *BARELY* GOT AWAY... IT'S *BLIGHT* BEHIND ALL OF THIS, AND--

I KNOW.

WAIT, WHERE *ARE* YOU?

AT THE *OTHER* OFFICE. CHECK THE *NEWS.*

"OTHER...?" OH.

WAYNE BUYS OVERWHELMING MAJORITY OF WAYNE-POWERS STOCK.

Ending Labor Unrest, "First P...

YOU WENT AHEAD AND BOUGHT BACK THE COMPANY *ANYWAY.* SCHWAY.

WHAT'S THE--*OW!*-- *SCENE* DOWN THERE?

UGLY. G. GLEN *GODFREY* HAS MY EMPLOYEES RILED UP AGAIN ON BLIGHT'S BEHALF, READY TO *RIOT.*

BUT I'M ABOUT TO PUT AN *END* TO IT.

YOU-- *OW!*-- WANT *ME* THERE?

NO. BECAUSE DEREK POWERS WILL BE IN A *RAGE* WHEN HE GETS THIS NEWS, AND HE *DOESN'T* KNOW I'M *DOWNTOWN.*

HE'LL BE COMING *THERE,* TO *KILL* ME.

UNDERSTOOD. THAT'LL GIVE ME TIME TO FIX MY *MASK* AFTER BLIGHT *BARBECUED* IT. TELL *ACE* HE OWES ME FOR PLAYING *WATCHDOG.*

JOJO

HI, MAX.

YOU'RE RIGHT ON TIME.

WAYNE-POWERS PENTHOUSE OFFICE ELEVATOR ACCESS REQUESTED. PROSPECTIVE PASSENGERS, ONE. IDENTI-SCAN: G. GLEN--

--GODFREY. LET HIM UP.

YOU'RE A *FOOLISH* OLD MAN, MR. WAYNE.

OH?

NEWS HASN'T SPREAD TO THE *STREETS* YET. IF I LET THOSE PEOPLE DOWN THERE KNOW THAT YOU'VE BOUGHT A *MASSIVE* CONTROLLING INTEREST IN THIS COMPANY...

...THAT THE MAN WHO'S *OPPRESSED* THEM FOR SO LONG HAS CLOSED HIS FIST *TIGHTER* AROUND THEIR THROATS...

...THEY'LL RIP THIS BUILDING RIGHT OUT FROM *UNDER* YOU.

IF HE KNOWS I'D COME AT HIM WITH AN *OXIDIZER*, HE'S *GOT* TO KNOW I'LL TRY TO *PIERCE* THE SUIT AGAIN.

SO HE'LL HAVE *UPGRADED* THE SUIT, WHICH HE FIGURES *I'LL* FIGURE, AND THAT I'LL HAVE *UPGRADED* THE BATARANGS... WHICH I *HAVE*.

BUT I *ONLY* NEED TO HIT HIM *ONCE*... SO IF I THROW *MORE* AT HIM THAN HE CAN MAYBE HANDLE...

FSHOOM

FSHOOM

MR. POWERS... DEREK... *NO!*

FRENCH!

THULKK

NOT SURE WHO *SLAG-IN-A-BAG* IS, BUT THE WOUND DOESN'T LOOK *FATAL*...

STILL, I CAN BET BLIGHT'S *NOT* GONNA BE--

--HAPPY.

YOU'RE ALL I... HAVE...

TZZARK

ENOUGH!

KUH!

YOU HAVE TAKEN *ENOUGH* FROM ME...YOU WON'T TAKE MY ONLY *FRIEND*, TOO!

I WILL MELT YOU INTO THE *SOIL!*

"YOU'RE... GIVING IN...?"

...BUT THE *SALARY DEMANDS*...THE *PENSION* AND *INSURANCE* INCREASES... THE *PROFIT-SHARING*...

THERE'S NO *WAY*...YOU *CAN'T*...! IT'D TAKE EVERY LAST PENNY YOU *HAVE!*

YOU'D BE *SURPRISED*, GODFREY. I HAVE SOME VERY *BIG PENNIES.*

I ORDERED *RATIFICATION* OF YOUR DEMANDS, PLUS AN *ADDITIONAL* TEN PERCENT ACROSS THE BOARD, AS YOU WERE WALKING INTO THE BUILDING.

I EXPECT WORD OF *THAT* HAS GOTTEN TO THE *GROUND FLOOR* BY NOW.

THE CROWDS. THE *PROTESTERS*... THEY'RE--

EXCELLENT *WORK*, GODFREY. YOU GOT MY EMPLOYEES *EVERYTHING* THEY WANTED AND *MORE.* YOU'RE A HERO. EXCEPT PERHAPS TO *DEREK POWERS.*

NOW, GET THE HELL *OUT* OF MY CITY.

OH, AND TELL YOUR *OTHER* BOSSES...YOUR *REAL* MASTERS... I EXPECT I'LL SEE THEM *SOON.*

TELL THEM I'LL BE *WAITING, PREPARED.*

AS ALWAYS.

"OH, I HOPE *WAYNE IS WATCHING...*"

THEY HAULED *BLIGHT* AWAY, BUT THEY COULDN'T TELL IF HE WAS *ALIVE* OR *DEAD*, BECAUSE SO MUCH OF HIM HAD...OOZED AWAY.

ANYWAY, ONCE *FRENCH* HEALS, HE'S OFF TO BLACKGATE. HE CAN PROBABLY *REDUCE* HIS SENTENCE IF HE HELPS CURE *OTHER* RADIATION-AFFLICTED METAS.

AND YOU REALLY *DID* IT, HUH? YOU GOT IT *ALL BACK*.

I HAD TO GIVE NEARLY EVERYTHING ELSE *AWAY* TO DO IT. THE *SUM TOTAL* OF THE WAYNE FORTUNE IS NOW TIED UP ALMOST COMPLETELY IN THIS *COMPANY*.

BUT THAT'S *ALL RIGHT*. IT CAN MAKE *MORE* MONEY HERE, AND FUND *OUR* MISSION *AND* OTHER WORTHY PROJECTS. THIS IS WHERE THE FORTUNE *BELONGS*.

AND *THIS* IS WHERE *I* BELONG NOW, AT LEAST *PART* OF THE TIME.

AFTER MANY, MANY YEARS, IT'S TIME FOR BRUCE WAYNE TO COME *OUT* OF THE SHADOWS.

A *LITTLE*.

TOMORROW, *"POWERS"* COMES OFF THE MASTHEAD AT *LAST*.

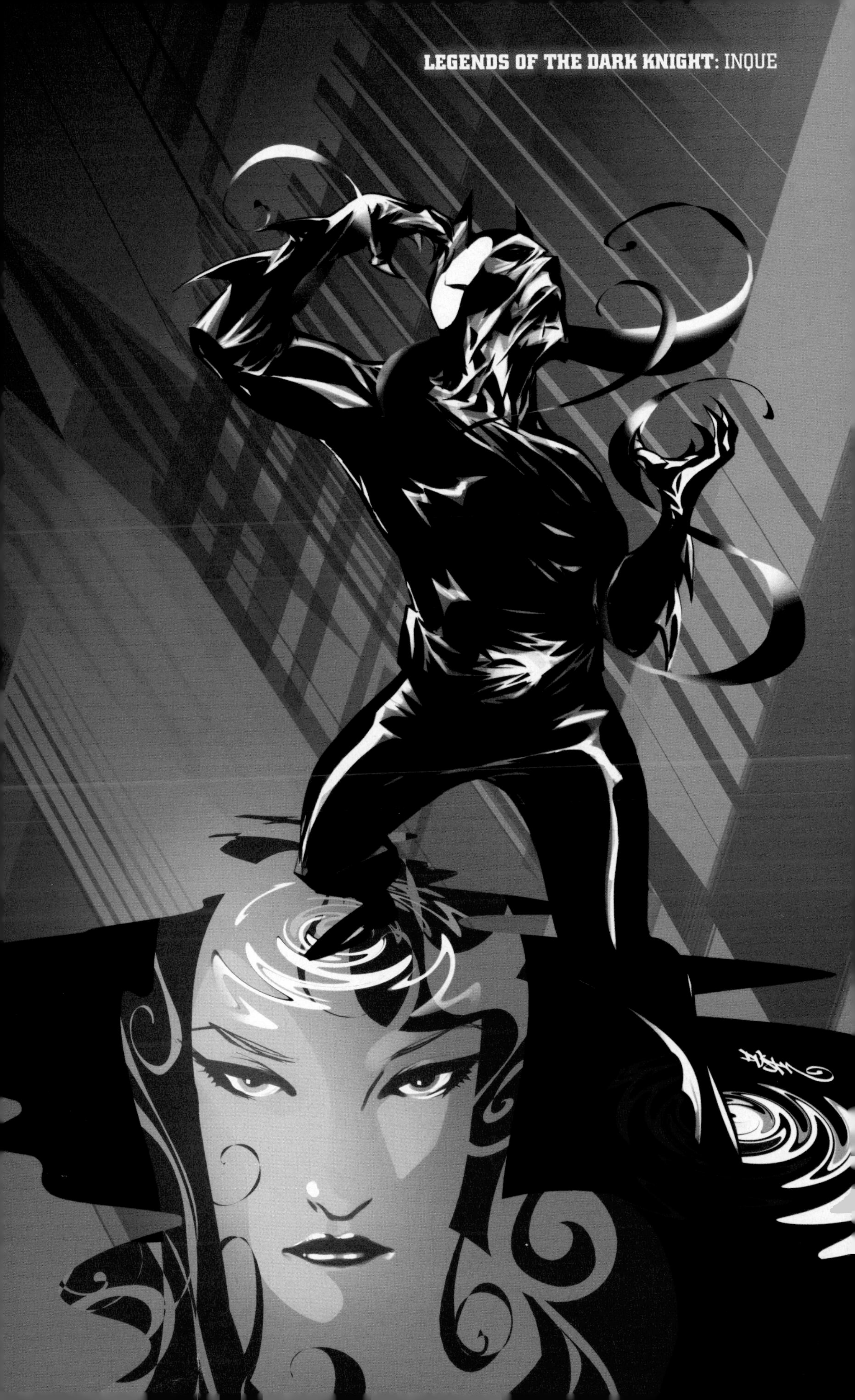

YOU THINK OF ME ONLY AS *INQUE*, A COLD-BLOODED MERCENARY...

DON'T FIRE! YOUR BULLETS WOULDN'T HARM HER, JUST WHAT SHE'S *HOLDING!*

SO WHAT'S THE *PLAN*, HERO? WE JUST LET HER TAKE *OFF* WITH IT?

NO...

...TURN UP YOUR *COLLARS*, SOLDIERS...

...IT'S ABOUT TO GET A LITTLE *CHILLY* IN HERE.

FWSSS

FWSSS

TKASSHH

KRSSHH

ICE?! ISN'T THAT SORT OF *OBVIOUS?* YOU'VE BEATEN HER THAT WAY *BEFORE*...

...BUT *ALL* YOU KNOW OF ME IS THE *SURFACE*. LIKE *ANY* POOL, I HAVE MY *DEPTHS*...

AFTER ALL THE *VIOLENCE* AND *PAIN* WE HAVE PUT EACH OTHER THROUGH, COULD YOU SHOW ME THAT *KINDNESS?*

SPLAMM

WHAT WOULD YOU DO IF YOU KNEW *EVERYTHING?*

UH.... BATMAN...?

PLASSHHH

CAN'T....CAN'T BREATHE....!

"UNIMPORTANT. SHE'S IN THE *WIND* AGAIN, AND SOON WE'LL CATCH HER FOR *GOOD*.

"THAT'S *ALL* WE NEED TO KNOW ABOUT HER."

I AM *WEAK* AND GROWING WEAKER, *FASTER*. DID YOU *KNOW* THAT?

IT IS THE *MUTAGEN* THAT MADE ME THIS WAY.

OR, RATHER, IT IS THE MUTAGEN THAT HAS MADE ME *WEAK*. IT IS NOT WHAT MADE ME WHAT *I* AM.

MY WORLD WAS *VERY SMALL* GROWING UP. I WAS *POOR* IN A POOR CITY, LIKE SO MANY *OTHERS*, DREAMING OF A *BETTER*, BIGGER LIFE IN A LAND CALLED *"SOMEWHERE ELSE."*

CIVIL WAR CAME TO MY COUNTRY WHEN I WAS BUT A YOUNG WOMAN, LITTLE MORE THAN A *GIRL*.

OUR HOME, OUR CITY, WAS ONE OF THE *FIRST* DESTROYED BY THE MADNESS.

WITH *TENS* OF *THOUSANDS* OF OTHER DISPOSSESSED PEOPLE, MY SMALL WORLD BECAME A *REFUGEE CAMP.* ALL I CARRIED WITH ME WAS A FEW POSSESSIONS AND MY DREAMS.

DISEASE NEARLY KILLED ME, AND *TWICE* NEARLY KILLED MY *FATHER.*

INTERNATIONAL AID WAS NOT ENOUGH TO KEEP US ALIVE.

FOR *THAT,* WE HAD NO CHOICE BUT TO TURN TO OUR CAMP'S *BLACK MARKET.*

OVER TIME, WE TRADED *EVERYTHING* WE HAD... BUT I *KEPT* MY DREAMS.

WHEN THE WAR CAME EVEN TO THE CAMP, OUR *CONTACTS* IN THE BLACK MARKET BECAME *CRUCIAL.*

THEY LED A SMALL BAND OF US *EAST* BY *MOONLIGHT,* HOPING TO REACH THE *COAST,* AND THE *PORTS.*

I DARED DREAM OF A *BOAT* THAT MIGHT CARRY ME OVER THE WATER TO MY BETTER, BIGGER "SOMEPLACE ELSE."

MY MOTHER NEVER SAW THE WATER.

I WAS PUT INTO *ANOTHER* CONTAINER, *ANOTHER* SMALL WORLD...

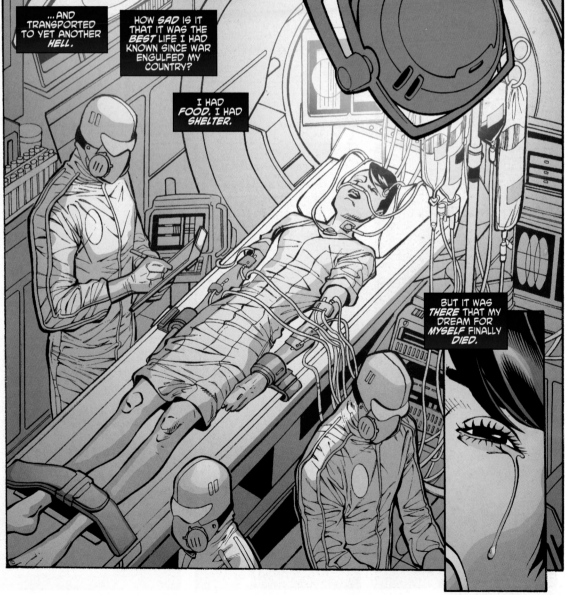

...AND TRANSPORTED TO YET ANOTHER *HELL.*

HOW *SAD* IS IT THAT IT WAS THE *BEST* LIFE I HAD KNOWN SINCE WAR ENGULFED MY COUNTRY?

I HAD *FOOD.* I HAD *SHELTER.*

BUT IT WAS *THERE* THAT MY DREAM FOR *MYSELF* FINALLY *DIED.*

THEY DID NOT *CARE* THAT I WAS PREGNANT. THEY THOUGHT IT... *INTERESTING*, AND WONDERED WHAT *EFFECT* IT WOULD HAVE ON THE *EXPERIMENTS*.

BUT THERE CAME A TIME WHEN THEY WERE CONVINCED I WOULD *DIE*. NO LONGER OF *USE* TO THEM, THEY SIMPLY RETURNED ME TO THE *STREETS*.

ANYONE I TRIED TO TELL OF MY *EXPERIENCES* CONSIDERED ME A *MADWOMAN*.

I *LIVED*. IN A *CHARITY WARD*, I HAD MY CHILD. A HEALTHY, STRONG, *NORMAL* GIRL.

IN *HER*, ALL OF MY DREAMS.

WE LIVED IN THE SHELTERS. I HAD *NO SKILLS*, *NO MONEY*, A *BARE* GRASP ON THE LANGUAGE, AND AN *INFANT*.

THERE WAS NO *HOPE* FOR PEOPLE SUCH AS US.

NO WAY FOR ME TO RAISE MY DAUGHTER TO THE LIFE I HAD ONCE DREAMED FOR *MYSELF*, NOW DREAMED ONLY FOR *HER*.

WHEN, *MONTHS* AFTER I HAD LEFT THE LABORATORY, THE EXPERIMENTS DONE THERE FINALLY *TOOK HOLD*, MY THOUGHTS WERE *ONLY* OF HER.

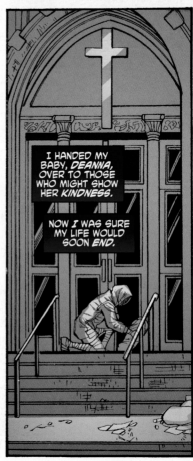

I HANDED MY BABY, *DEANNA*, OVER TO THOSE WHO MIGHT SHOW HER *KINDNESS*.

NOW *I* WAS SURE MY LIFE WOULD SOON *END*.

I WENT *BACK* TO THE SHELTER. AND WAITED TO *DIE*.

BUT AGAIN, I DID *NOT*.

I *CHANGED*. OVER TIME, I LEARNED TO *CONTROL* IT.

I PICTURED A *PATH* I MIGHT TRAVEL, AND WHILE IT DID *NOT* INCLUDE A WAY TO BE A *GOOD MOTHER*...

...I *DID* SEE A WAY TO MAKE A *LIFE* FOR MY DAUGHTER, TO MAYBE *LIFT* HER TOWARD THE DREAM I'D HAD FOR HER, EVEN IF I COULD ONLY DO IT FROM *AFAR*.

I HAD A *SERVICE* I COULD SELL, A *PRICE* I COULD NAME.

I BECAME *VERY* GOOD, *VERY* QUICKLY.

AND VERY WELL *COMPENSATED*.

WELL ENOUGH TO KEEP *TRACK* OF MY LITTLE GIRL OVER THE YEARS, AND ANONYMOUSLY ENSURE SHE WOULD HAVE *EVERYTHING* SHE NEEDED IN LIFE.

ANONYMOUSLY, BECAUSE I DIDN'T WANT HER TO THINK OF HER MOTHER AS *MORE* OF A MONSTER THAN SURELY SHE *ALREADY* DID.

WHEN I THOUGHT SHE MIGHT BE *OLD* ENOUGH TO UNDERSTAND, I *REVEALED* MYSELF TO HER. I WAS *WRONG*.

SHE WOULD NEVER UNDERSTAND.

SHE WANTED *NOTHING* FROM ME SAVE THE *MONEY*.

FILLED WITH *SHAME*, *GUILT*, AND A DESIRE TO BE PART OF HER LIFE *SOMEHOW*, I CONTINUED TO *PROVIDE* IT. AND I STAYED *AWAY*.

UNTIL MY CONDITION *WORSENED* THANKS TO THE POISONS INSIDE ME, AND I BEGAN TO LOSE *COHESION*.

I NEEDED *MORE* AND *MORE* OF THE MUTAGEN THE SCIENTISTS HAD GIVEN ME YEARS AGO. AT A TIME WHEN I WAS UNABLE TO OBTAIN IT *MYSELF*, I TURNED TO THE ONE PERSON I THOUGHT MIGHT *HELP* ME.

I WAS *BETRAYED*, INSTEAD. I COULD NOT *BLAME* ANYONE BUT *MYSELF*, AND I COULD *NOT* STOP *LOVING* MY CHILD.

BARELY ABLE TO HOLD TOGETHER, I TOOK JOBS WITH *MUTAGEN* AS *PAYMENT*, AND SPENT EVERY SPARE MOMENT WATCHING OVER THE ONE WHO BETRAYED ME.

THE ONE IN WHOM MY DREAM *STILL* LIVES.

I STILL DREAM FOR MY CHILD.

I AM *HERE.*

I HAVE BROUGHT WHAT YOU *REQUESTED.* NOW GIVE ME MY *PAYMENT.*

NAW. WE *HEARD* ABOUT YOU. TIME WAS, *EVERYBODY* WAS SCARED OF YOU, BUT YOU AIN'T WHAT YOU *USED* TO BE.

YOU'RE GONNA *GIVE* US THAT TRIGGER. *THAT'S IT.*

NO.

BBRRTTT

BBRRTTT

KESSHHH

KESSHHH

KEESSHHH

SLLSSKK

SLSSKK

SLSSKK

SSSLLSS

OH, VERY WELL... I HAD HOPED *PERHAPS* I COULD LEAVE HERE WITH *BOTH* THE TRIGGER AND THE MUTAGEN, BUT I CAN ALWAYS *COVER* THE DISAPPEARANCE OF SO SMALL A SAMPLE.

WITH MY DREAM, I PASSED ON MY *SICKNESS*.

IT ROSE TO THE SURFACE ONLY IN *RECENT MONTHS.*

MY DAUGHTER, *DESPITE* ALL HER JUSTIFIABLE ANGER AND HATRED, *STILL* NEEDS HER *MOTHER.*

A MOTHER WHO, DESPITE ALL THE *INJUSTICES* AND *BETRAYALS,* STILL DREAMS FOR HER *DAUGHTER.*

OH, DEANNA, MY BEAUTIFUL BABY GIRL...

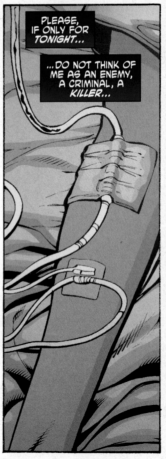

PLEASE, IF ONLY FOR *TONIGHT*...

...DO NOT THINK OF ME AS AN ENEMY, A CRIMINAL, A *KILLER*...

PLEASE, NOW THAT YOU KNOW THE *WHOLE* STORY, THE *HIDDEN DEPTHS* OF THE POOL...

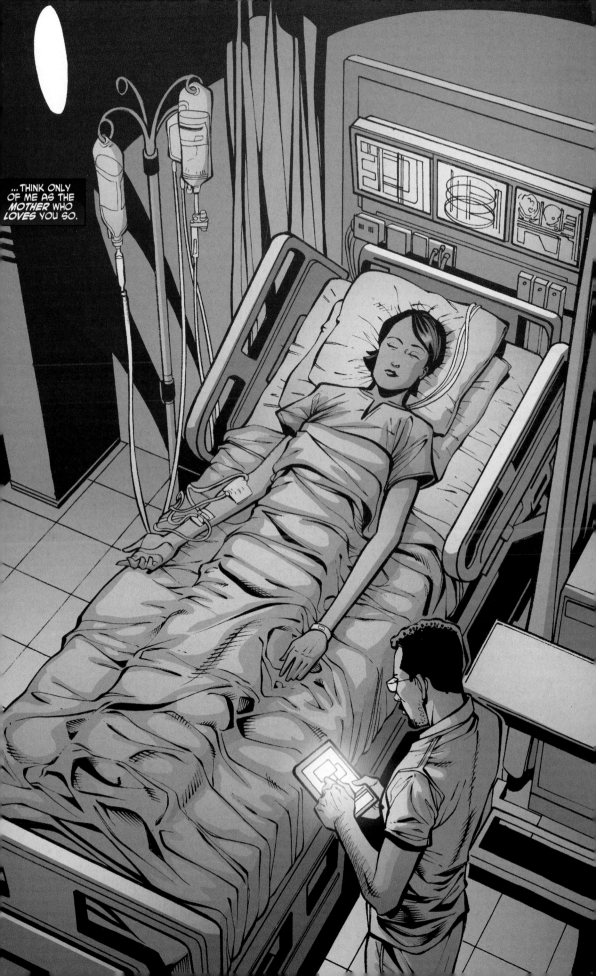

...THINK ONLY OF ME AS THE *MOTHER* WHO *LOVES* YOU SO.

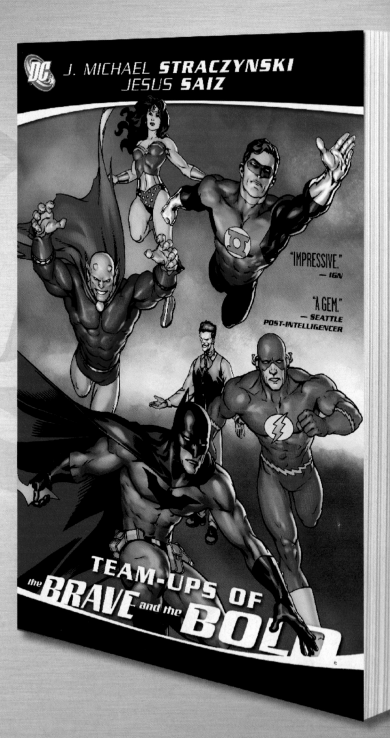

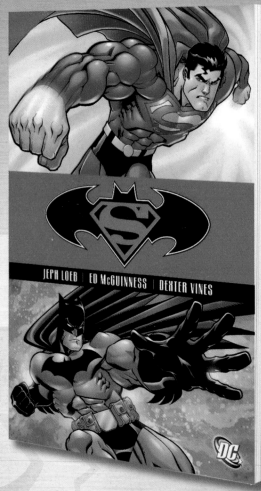